Andrew Brodie ✔

Mental Maths Tests

for ages 10 – 11

✓ **Ten complete Mental Maths timed tests, together with a pre-recorded CD**

✓ **Ideal practice for National Tests**

✓ **Bonus material includes multiplication and addition grids for additional practice**

General instructions for the administration of the tests

To make these tests seem as realistic as possible children should have clear desks and only a pen or pencil to write with. They should not be supplied with paper for working out the answers.

Before starting each test the children should write their name and school in the spaces provided.

Inform the children that:

- they should work individually and should not talk at all during the test;

- they will be allowed 5 seconds to answer each of the first five questions, 10 seconds for each of the next set of questions and 15 seconds for each of the last set of questions;

- for some questions, some information will be provided on the test sheet;

- calculators or other equipment are not allowed;

- they should not rub out answers but, if they wish to change them, they can cross them out and write their new answers next to the incorrect ones;

- if they cannot do a question they should put a cross in the answer box.

Test 1

Before playing the test on the CD give each child a copy of the test and read out the following script:

Listen to the instructions carefully. I will answer any questions that you have after I have finished reading the instructions to you. Once the test starts you will not be able to ask any questions.

The first question is a practice question. In the test there will then be twenty questions.

Every question has an answer box. Make sure that you only write the answer to the correct question in the box. Try to work out each answer in your head. You can make notes outside the answer box if this helps you but do not try to write out calculations because you will not have enough time. For some questions you will find important information already provided for you.

Each question will be read out twice. Listen carefully, then work out your answer. If you cannot do the question, just put a cross. If you make a mistake, do not rub out the wrong answer; cross it out and write the correct answer.

Some questions are easy and some are more difficult. Do not worry if you find a question hard; just do your best. I hope that you enjoy the test.

At this point, answer any questions that the children ask.

Now listen carefully to the practice question. You will hear the question twice, then you will have five seconds to work out and write down the answer.

What is twelve add eight?

What is twelve add eight?

Allow the children five seconds to write the answer, then say:

Put your pen down.

Check that the children have written the answer to the practice question in the practice question answer box. Remind them that they cannot ask any more questions once the test is started. When you are ready, press start on your CD player. When the test is finished ask the children to stop writing, then collect the test sheets. For ease of marking we have created a copy of the test paper with the answers entered in the appropriate boxes.

Questions for Test 1

For each of the first five questions you have five seconds to work out and write down the answer.

1   How many tens in eighty?

2   What is the total of twelve and six?

3   What number is double twenty?

4   Subtract thirteen from twenty.

5   Look at your test sheet.
Which of these numbers is an odd number?

For each of the next questions you have ten seconds to work out and write down the answer.

6   What number is half of sixty-four?

7   How many metres are there in one kilometre?

8   Subtract seventy-four pence from one pound.

9   Look at your answer sheet.
What number is the arrow pointing to?

10   What number is double two and a half?

11   Look at your test sheet.
Put a tick by the name of the shape.

12   A chocolate bar costs forty-three pence.
What is the cost of two chocolate bars?

13   How many days are there in four weeks?

14   A P.E. lesson starts at one fifteen and finishes at two o'clock.
How many minutes does the lesson last?

15   What is the product of six and eight?

For each of the next questions you have fifteen seconds to work out and write down the answer.

16   Find the total of thirteen, fourteen and fifteen.

17   Look at your test sheet.
Circle the two amounts that add up to £38.

18   Half of a number is nine and a half.
What is the number?

19   Divide sixty-four by four.

20   A rectangle measures six centimetres by four centimetres.
What is the area of the rectangle?

Put your pen down. The test is over.

Andrew Brodie: Mental Maths Tests 10–11 © A & C Black

Test 1

First name .... Last name ....

School ....

....   **Total marks**

Practice question

Five-second questions

| 1 | | 80 |

| 2 | | 12   6 |

| 3 | |

| 4 | | 13   20 |

| 5 | 24   30   19   12 |

Ten-second questions

| 6 | | 64 |

| 7 | metres |

| 8 | | 74p |

| 9 |

2•2 ↓ 2•8

| 10 | | $2\frac{1}{2}$ |

| 11 | | hexagon ☐
 triangle ☐
 square ☐
 pentagon ☐
 octagon ☐ |

| 12 | pence | 43p |

| 13 | days |

| 14 | minutes | 1.15pm 2pm |

| 15 | | 6   8 |

Fifteen-second questions

| 16 | | 13 14 15 |

| 17 | £40   £14   £24   £4 |

| 18 | | $9\frac{1}{2}$ |

| 19 | | 64 |

| 20 | cm² |

Practice question

	20

Five-second questions

1	**8**	80

2	**18**	12 6

3	**40**

4	**7**	13 20

5	24 30 ⑲ 12

Ten-second questions

6	**32**	64

7	**1000** metres

8	**26p**	74p

9	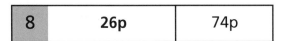
	2.6

10	**5**	$2\frac{1}{2}$

11		hexagon ☐
		triangle ☐
		square ☐
		pentagon ☑
		octagon ☐

12	**86** pence	43p

13	**28** days

14	**45** metres	1.15 pm

15	**48**	6 8

Fifteen-second questions

16	**42**	13 14 15

17	£40 (£14) (£24) £4

18	**19**	$9\frac{1}{2}$

19	**16**	64

20	**24** cm²

Test 2

Before playing the test on the CD give each child a copy of the test and read out the following script:

Listen to the instructions carefully. I will answer any questions that you have after I have finished reading the instructions to you. Once the test starts you will not be able to ask any questions.

The first question is a practice question. In the test there will then be twenty questions.

Every question has an answer box. Make sure that you only write the answer to the correct question in the box. Try to work out each answer in your head. You can make notes outside the answer box if this helps you but do not try to write out calculations because you will not have enough time. For some questions you will find important information already provided for you.

Each question will be read out twice. Listen carefully, then work out your answer. If you cannot do the question, just put a cross. If you make a mistake, do not rub out the wrong answer; cross it out and write the correct answer.

Some questions are easy and some are more difficult. Do not worry if you find a question hard; just do your best. I hope that you enjoy the test.

At this point, answer any questions that the children ask.

Now listen carefully to the practice question. You will hear the question twice, then you will have five seconds to work out and write down the answer.

What is seven add four?

What is seven add four?

Allow the children five seconds to write the answer, then say:

Put your pen down.

Check that the children have written the answer to the practice question in the practice question answer box. Remind them that they cannot ask any more questions once the test is started. When you are ready, press start on your CD player. When the test is finished ask the children to stop writing, then collect the test sheets. For ease of marking we have created a copy of the test paper with the answers entered in the appropriate boxes.

Questions for Test 2

For each of the first five questions you have five seconds to work out and write down the answer.

1 Multiply seven by three.

2 What is the sum of four and nine?

3 How many fives make thirty?

4 Multiply fifty-six by ten.

5 If I spend seventy-five pounds, how much change do I get from one hundred pounds?

For each of the next questions you have ten seconds to work out and write down the answer.

6 Look at your test sheet.
Add the two odd numbers together.

7 Look at your test sheet.
What fraction of the circle is shaded?

8 What number is double fifty-six?

9 What fraction is a half add a quarter?

10 How many ten pound notes are in one hundred and forty pounds?

11 How many times larger is three thousand seven hundred than thirty-seven?

12 How many minutes are there in three hours?

13 What is four point seven add three point five?

14 If I save eight pounds per month how much money will I have after one year?

15 Look at your test sheet.
Put a tick by the name of the shape.

For each of the next questions you have fifteen seconds to work out and write down the answer.

16 Look at your test sheet.
What is the perimeter of the shape?

17 How many seconds are there in fifteen minutes?

18 What is the next number in this sequence: one, four, nine, sixteen?

19 What number is one quarter of thirty-two?

20 How much is fifty per cent of one hundred and seventy pounds?

Put your pen down. The test is over.

Test 2

First name .... Last name ....

School ....

.... **Total marks**

Practice question

Five-second questions

1	

2	

3	

4	56

5	£	£75

Ten-second questions

6	13 16 19

7	

8	56

9	$\frac{1}{2}$ $\frac{1}{4}$

10	£140

11	3700 37

12	minutes

13	4.7 3.5

14	£	£8

15		hexagon ☐
		triangle ☐
		square ☐
		pentagon ☐
		octagon ☐

Fifteen-second questions

16	2 cm, 1 cm, 3 cm, 3 cm, 2 cm, 5 cm
	cm

17	seconds

18	1 4 9 16

19	32

20	£	£170

Test 2 Answers

Practice question

10	**11**

Five-second questions

1	**21**	
2	**13**	
3	**6**	
4	**560**	56
5	**£25**	£75

Ten-second questions

6	**13** **16** **19**
	32

7	$\frac{1}{3}$	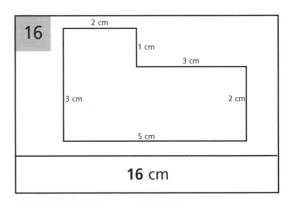

8	**112**	56
9	$\frac{3}{4}$	$\frac{1}{2}$ $\frac{1}{4}$
10	**14**	£140
11	**one hundred times**	3700 37

12	**180** minutes

13	**8.2**	4.7 3.5
14	**£96**	£8

15	hexagon ✔
	triangle ☐
	square ☐
	pentagon ☐
	octagon ☐

Fifteen-second questions

16	2 cm / 1 cm / 3 cm / 3 cm / 2 cm / 5 cm
	16 cm

17	**900** seconds

18	**25**	1 4 9 16
19	**8**	32
20	**£85**	£170

Andrew Brodie: Mental Maths Tests 10–11 © A & C Black

Test 3

Before playing the test on the CD give each child a copy of the test and read out the following script:

Listen to the instructions carefully. I will answer any questions that you have after I have finished reading the instructions to you. Once the test starts you will not be able to ask any questions.

The first question is a practice question. In the test there will then be twenty questions.

Every question has an answer box. Make sure that you only write the answer to the correct question in the box. Try to work out each answer in your head. You can make notes outside the answer box if this helps you but do not try to write out calculations because you will not have enough time. For some questions you will find important information already provided for you.

Each question will be read out twice. Listen carefully, then work out your answer. If you cannot do the question, just put a cross. If you make a mistake, do not rub out the wrong answer; cross it out and write the correct answer.

Some questions are easy and some are more difficult. Do not worry if you find a question hard; just do your best. I hope that you enjoy the test.

At this point, answer any questions that the children ask.

Now listen carefully to the practice question. You will hear the question twice, then you will have five seconds to work out and write down the answer.

What is two times six?

What is two times six?

Allow the children five seconds to write the answer, then say:

Put your pen down.

Check that the children have written the answer to the practice question in the practice question answer box. Remind them that they cannot ask any more questions once the test is started. When you are ready, press start on your CD player. When the test is finished ask the children to stop writing, then collect the test sheets. For ease of marking we have created a copy of the test paper with the answers entered in the appropriate boxes.

Questions for Test 3

For each of the first five questions you have five seconds to work out and write down the answer.

1   Divide twenty-four by six.

2   Subtract sixteen from thirty.

3   Add eighteen to nineteen.

4   How many minutes are there in two hours?

5   What is three quarters of twelve?

For each of the next questions you have ten seconds to work out and write down the answer.

6   Add together twelve, thirteen and fourteen.

7   A chocolate bar costs forty-two pence to buy.
    How much change would there be from a pound?

8   Find a half of six point four.

9   Each side of a square is three centimetres long.
    What is the perimeter of the square?

10   Look at your test sheet.
     What fraction of the diagram is shaded?

11   What is one hundred and fifteen divided by five?

12   Give the mean of ten, sixteen and nineteen.

13   What temperature is ten degrees higher than minus two degrees Celsius?

14   Look at your test sheet.
     Put a ring around the number that is half of one hundred and sixty-two.

15   What is two point four multiplied by three?

For each of the next questions you have fifteen seconds to work out and write down the answer.

16   Multiply two point zero four by one hundred.

17   A square has an area of thirty-six square centimetres. How long is each side?

18   Look at your test sheet.
     The diagram shows an equilateral triangle.
     What is the size of the angle marked *x* ?

19   Write the number which is three quarters of sixty.

20   Look at your test sheet.
     Circle the numbers that are factors of twelve.

Put your pen down. The test is over.

Andrew Brodie: Mental Maths Tests 10–11 © A & C Black

Test 3

First name .... Last name ....

School ....

.... **Total marks**

Practice question

Five-second questions

1		24
2		30
3		18 19
4	minutes	
5		12

Ten-second questions

6		12 13 14
7	pence	42p
8		6.4
9	cm	

10	

11		115

12		10 16 19
13	°c	-2°c
14	81 162 91 324	
15		2.4

Fifteen-second questions

16		2.04
17	cm	36 cm²

18	°

19		60

20	3 7 4
	5 8 10
	36 24 2

Test 3 Answers

Practice question

	12

Five-second questions

1	**4**	24

2	**14**	30

3	**37**	18 19

4	**120** minutes

5	**9**	12

Ten-second questions

6	**39**	12 13 14

7	**58** pence	42p

8	**3.2**	6.4

9	**12** cm

10	$\frac{2}{3}$	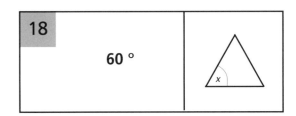

11	**23**	115

12	**15**	10 16 19

13	**8** °c	-2 °c

14	(**81**) 162 91 324

15	**7.2**	2.4

Fifteen-second questions

16	**204**	2.04

17	**6** cm	36 cm²

18	**60** °	

19	**45**	60

20	(**3**) 7 (**4**) 5 8 10 36 24 (**2**)

Test 4

Before playing the test on the CD give each child a copy of the test and read out the following script:

Listen to the instructions carefully. I will answer any questions that you have after I have finished reading the instructions to you. Once the test starts you will not be able to ask any questions.

The first question is a practice question. In the test there will then be twenty questions.

Every question has an answer box. Make sure that you only write the answer to the correct question in the box. Try to work out each answer in your head. You can make notes outside the answer box if this helps you but do not try to write out calculations because you will not have enough time. For some questions you will find important information already provided for you.

Each question will be read out twice. Listen carefully, then work out your answer. If you cannot do the question, just put a cross. If you make a mistake, do not rub out the wrong answer; cross it out and write the correct answer.

Some questions are easy and some are more difficult. Do not worry if you find a question hard; just do your best. I hope that you enjoy the test.

At this point, answer any questions that the children ask.

Now listen carefully to the practice question. You will hear the question twice, then you will have five seconds to work out and write down the answer.

What is three times four?

What is three times four?

Allow the children five seconds to write the answer, then say:

Put your pen down.

Check that the children have written the answer to the practice question in the practice question answer box. Remind them that they cannot ask any more questions once the test is started. When you are ready, press start on your CD player. When the test is finished ask the children to stop writing, then collect the test sheets. For ease of marking we have created a copy of the test paper with the answers entered in the appropriate boxes.

Questions for Test 4

For each of the first five questions you have five seconds to work out and write down the answer.

1 Write the next term in this sequence: two, four, six, eight.

2 Look at your test sheet.
Draw a ring around the number three hundred and sixty-two.

3 Multiply thirty-seven by ten.

4 What is thirty-five divided by seven?

5 What is the total of sixteen and fourteen?

For each of the next questions you have ten seconds to work out and write down the answer.

6 What number is six tenths of forty?

7 Write two hundred and fifty grams in kilograms.

8 What is the value of seven squared?

9 Look at your test sheet.
Ring the number that shows one quarter as a decimal fraction.

10 Find double twenty-eight.

11 Decrease eighty-four by thirty-two.

12 Four hundred add three hundred add two hundred.

13 Look at your test sheet.
Draw a ring around the number fifty-seven thousand and seventeen.

14 How many years are there in six decades?

15 I used four hundred and fifty millilitres from a two-litre bottle. How much is left?

For each of the next questions you have fifteen seconds to work out and write down the answer.

16 Look at your test sheet.
What is the size of the angle marked *x*?

17 A camera at half price costs one hundred and forty-six pounds.
What was the full price?

18 A train leaves at nine forty-five a.m. and arrives at ten twenty-five a.m.
How long does the journey take in minutes?

19 A t-shirt costs twenty pounds. It is reduced by 25%.
What is the new price?

20 Double 1.6, then add 0.8.

Put your pen down. The test is over.

Test 4

First name .... Last name ....

School ....

....

Total marks

Practice question

Five-second questions

| 1 | | 2 4 6 8 |

| 2 | 316   632   326   362 |

| 3 | | 37 |

| 4 | | 35 |

| 5 | | 16   14 |

Ten-second questions

| 6 | | 40 |

| 7 | kilograms |

| 8 | |

| 9 | 0.5   0.75   0.25   0.125 |

| 10 | | 28 |

| 11 | | 84   32 |

| 12 | |

| 13 | 57017   57070   5717 |

| 14 | |

| 15 | ml | 450 ml |

Fifteen-second questions

| 16 |

x 108°

°

| 17 | £ | £146 |

| 18 | |

| 19 | £ | £20 |

| 20 | | 1.6   0.8 |

Test 4 Answers

Practice question

	12

Five-second questions

1	10	2 4 6 8

2	316 632 326 (362)

3	370	37

4	5	35

5	30	16 14

Ten-second questions

6	24	40

7	0.25 kilograms

8	49

9	0.5 0.75 (0.25) 0.125

10	56	28

11	52	84 32

12	900

13	(57017) 57070 5717

14	60

15	1550 ml	450 ml

Fifteen-second questions

16	
	x \ 108°
72°	

17	£292	£146

18	40 minutes

19	£15	£20

20	4	1.6 0.8

Test 5

Before playing the test on the CD give each child a copy of the test and read out the following script:

Listen to the instructions carefully. I will answer any questions that you have after I have finished reading the instructions to you. Once the test starts you will not be able to ask any questions.

The first question is a practice question. In the test there will then be twenty questions.

Every question has an answer box. Make sure that you only write the answer to the correct question in the box. Try to work out each answer in your head. You can make notes outside the answer box if this helps you but do not try to write out calculations because you will not have enough time. For some questions you will find important information already provided for you.

Each question will be read out twice. Listen carefully, then work out your answer. If you cannot do the question, just put a cross. If you make a mistake, do not rub out the wrong answer; cross it out and write the correct answer.

Some questions are easy and some are more difficult. Do not worry if you find a question hard; just do your best. I hope that you enjoy the test.

At this point, answer any questions that the children ask.

Now listen carefully to the practice question. You will hear the question twice, then you will have five seconds to work out and write down the answer.

What is five times five?

What is five times five?

Allow the children five seconds to write the answer, then say:

Put your pen down.

Check that the children have written the answer to the practice question in the practice question answer box. Remind them that they cannot ask any more questions once the test is started. When you are ready, press start on your CD player. When the test is finished ask the children to stop writing, then collect the test sheets. For ease of marking we have created a copy of the test paper with the answers entered in the appropriate boxes.

Questions for Test 5

For each of the first five questions you have five seconds to work out and write down the answer.

1   What is sixteen add twelve?

2   What is the square of three?

3   What number is eight less than twenty-two?

4   How much is seven times nine?

5   Find the value of thirty-two divided by four.

For each of the next questions you have ten seconds to work out and write down the answer.

6   Write six centimetres in metres.

7   Look at your test sheet.
           What is the area of the rectangle?

8   How much is ten per cent of sixty pounds?

9   Find the total of five hundred and six hundred.

10   What is the value of double three point five?

11   What number is three hundred less than six hundred and forty?

12   Look at your test sheet.
           What percentage of the shape is shaded?

13   What is the total of thirty, forty and fifty?

14   Decrease seventy-five by twenty-three.

15   What is the product of twenty-five and three?

For each of the next questions you have fifteen seconds to work out and write down the answer.

16   Look at the price list on your test sheet.
           Jade spent two pounds and six pence. Which two items did she buy?

17   A bucket holds five litres.
           A jug holds half a litre.
           How many jugs of water will fill the bucket?

18   A square has sides of six point five centimetres.
           What is its perimeter?

19   I buy one item for four pounds fifty pence and one item for six pounds fifty pence.
           How much change do I have from twenty pounds?

20   Look at your test sheet.
           What size is the angle marked x?

Put your pen down. The test is over.

Test 5

First name .... Last name ....

School ....

.... **Total marks** [ ]

Practice question

[|]

Five-second questions

1		16 12
2		3
3		8 22
4		9
5		32

Ten-second questions

6	m	6 cm

7	

8 m × 3 m

8	£	£60
9		500 600
10		3.5
11		640

12	%	

13		30 40 50
14		75 23
15		25 3

Fifteen-second questions

16		Coffee £1.25 Tea £1.15 Cake £1.45 Biscuit 81p

17	

18	cm	6.5 cm
19	£	£20

20	°	33° x

Test 5 Answers

Practice question

25

Five-second questions

1	**28**	16	12

2	**9**	3

3	**14**	8	22

4	**63**	9

5	**8**	32

Ten-second questions

6	**0.06** m	6 cm

7		

8 m

3 m

24 m²

8	£6	£60

9	**1100**	500	600

10	**7**	3.5

11	**340**	640

12	**25%**	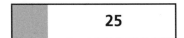

13	**120**	30	40	50

14	**52**	75	23

15	**75**	25	3

Fifteen-second questions

16	**Coffee and Biscuit**	Coffee £1.25 Tea £1.15 Cake £1.45 Biscuit 81p

17	**10**

18	**26** cm	6.5 cm

19	**£9.00**	£20

20	**57°**	

x

33°

Test 6

Before playing the test on the CD give each child a copy of the test and read out the following script:

Listen to the instructions carefully. I will answer any questions that you have after I have finished reading the instructions to you. Once the test starts you will not be able to ask any questions.

The first question is a practice question. In the test there will then be twenty questions.

Every question has an answer box. Make sure that you only write the answer to the correct question in the box. Try to work out each answer in your head. You can make notes outside the answer box if this helps you but do not try to write out calculations because you will not have enough time. For some questions you will find important information already provided for you.

Each question will be read out twice. Listen carefully, then work out your answer. If you cannot do the question, just put a cross. If you make a mistake, do not rub out the wrong answer; cross it out and write the correct answer.

Some questions are easy and some are more difficult. Do not worry if you find a question hard; just do your best. I hope that you enjoy the test.

At this point, answer any questions that the children ask.

Now listen carefully to the practice question. You will hear the question twice, then you will have five seconds to work out and write down the answer.

What is double six?

What is double six?

Allow the children five seconds to write the answer, then say:

Put your pen down.

Check that the children have written the answer to the practice question in the practice question answer box. Remind them that they cannot ask any more questions once the test is started. When you are ready, press start on your CD player. When the test is finished ask the children to stop writing, then collect the test sheets. For ease of marking we have created a copy of the test paper with the answers entered in the appropriate boxes.

Questions for Test 6

For each of the first five questions you have five seconds to work out and write down the answer.

1   What is the sum of three, two and six?

2   How much is seven times four?

3   Find the value of forty-eight divided by six.

4   Calculate four squared.

5   How many kilograms are there in half a tonne?

For each of the next questions you have ten seconds to work out and write down the answer.

6   What number is three quarters of forty?

7   How much is thirty per cent of one pound?

8   What is the value of double ninety-two?

9   What is four hundred and seventeen subtract one hundred and six?

10   Divide six into fifty-four.

11   Look at your test sheet.
What volume of water is shown in the measuring cylinder?

12   Look at your test sheet.
What is the perimeter of the rectangle?

13   How many years are there in three centuries?

14   Write two thousand four hundred and seventy-nine grams in kilograms.

15   How many days are there in March?

For each of the next questions you have fifteen seconds to work out and write down the answer.

16   The temperature at six o'clock was six degrees Celsius.
At midnight it had fallen by seven degrees Celsius.
What was the temperature at midnight?

17   Look at your test sheet.
Put a tick by the word that describes the triangle.

18   I spill nought point seven five litres from a one litre bottle.
How many millilitres are left in the bottle?

19   I spend five pounds seventy-five pence and three pounds ninety pence.
How much is this altogether?

20   Make the biggest integer you can using the digits three, five and seven.

Put your pen down. The test is over.

Andrew Brodie: Mental Maths Tests 10–11 © A & C Black

Test 6

First name .... Last name ....

School ....

.... **Total marks**

Practice question

Five-second questions

| 1 | | 3 | 2 | 6 |

| 2 | |

| 3 | | 48 |

| 4 | | 4 |

| 5 | | kg |

Ten-second questions

| 6 | | 40 |

| 7 | | 30% |

| 8 | | 92 |

| 9 | | 417 |

| 10 | | 54 |

| 11 | ml | (measuring cylinder: 500 ml scale, marks at 100, 200, 300, 400, 500, filled to 200) |

| 12 | 8 m / 3 m (rectangle) |
| | m |

| 13 | | years |

| 14 | | kg | 2479 g |

| 15 | | days |

Fifteen-second questions

| 16 | | °C | 6 °C |

| 17 | (triangle) | equilateral ☐ scalene ☐ isosceles ☐ |

| 18 | | ml |

| 19 | £ |

| 20 | | 3 | 5 | 7 |

Practice question

	12

Five-second questions

1	11	3	2	6

2	28

3	8	48

4	16	4

5	500 kg

Ten-second questions

6	30	40

7	30p	30%

8	184	92

9	311	417

10	9	54

11	220 ml	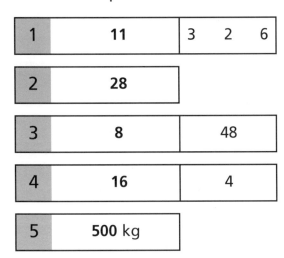

12	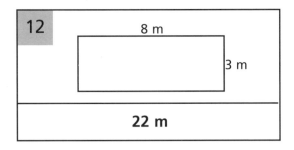 8 m, 3 m, **22 m**

13	300 years

14	2.479 kg	2479 g

15	31 days

Fifteen-second questions

16	-1 °C	6 °C

17	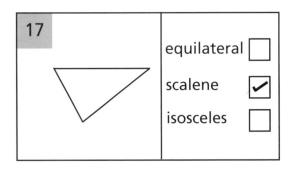 equilateral ☐, scalene ✔, isosceles ☐

18	250 ml

19	£9.65

20	753	3	5	7

Test 7

Before playing the test on the CD give each child a copy of the test and read out the following script:

Listen to the instructions carefully. I will answer any questions that you have after I have finished reading the instructions to you. Once the test starts you will not be able to ask any questions.

The first question is a practice question. In the test there will then be twenty questions.

Every question has an answer box. Make sure that you only write the answer to the correct question in the box. Try to work out each answer in your head. You can make notes outside the answer box if this helps you but do not try to write out calculations because you will not have enough time. For some questions you will find important information already provided for you.

Each question will be read out twice. Listen carefully, then work out your answer. If you cannot do the question, just put a cross. If you make a mistake, do not rub out the wrong answer; cross it out and write the correct answer.

Some questions are easy and some are more difficult. Do not worry if you find a question hard; just do your best. I hope that you enjoy the test.

At this point, answer any questions that the children ask.

Now listen carefully to the practice question. You will hear the question twice, then you will have five seconds to work out and write down the answer.

What is half of eight?

What is half of eight?

Allow the children five seconds to write the answer, then say:

Put your pen down.

Check that the children have written the answer to the practice question in the practice question answer box. Remind them that they cannot ask any more questions once the test is started. When you are ready, press start on your CD player. When the test is finished ask the children to stop writing, then collect the test sheets. For ease of marking we have created a copy of the test paper with the answers entered in the appropriate boxes.

Questions for Test 7

For each of the first five questions you have five seconds to work out and write down the answer.

1 Look at your test sheet.
Is the angle acute or obtuse?

2 Multiply seventeen by ten.

3 What is the next number in the sequence eleven, fourteen, seventeen, twenty?

4 Decrease eighteen by twelve.

5 How much is half of thirty?

For each of the next questions you have ten seconds to work out and write down the answer.

6 Look at your test sheet.
What fraction of the shape is shaded?

7 What number is three quarters of forty-eight?

8 Find the total of twenty-one plus thirty-one plus forty-one.

9 How many metres are there in three quarters of a kilometre?

10 What is six point five divided by ten?

11 A pencil costs thirty-five pence.
What is the cost of three pencils?

12 Look at your test sheet.
Add the even numbers together.

13 What is the remainder when fifty-one is divided by eight?

14 Find the value of double six point seven.

15 How many lengths of ten centimetres can you cut from a piece of string ninety-two centimetres long?

For each of the next questions you have fifteen seconds to work out and write down the answer.

16 How much is thirteen squared?

17 Look at your test sheet.
What is the size of the angle marked *x*?

18 Look at your test sheet.
What is the area of the rectangle?

19 I spend fourteen pounds eighty-six pence.
How much change do I get from twenty pounds?

20 A train leaves at ten fifty-five a.m. and arrives at its destination at one fifteen p.m.
How long is the journey?

Put your pen down. The test is over.

        Andrew Brodie: Mental Maths Tests 10–11 © A & C Black

Test 7

First name .... Last name ....

School ....

....

Total marks

Practice question

Five-second questions

1

angle

2

3 | 11, 14, 17, 20

4 | 18

5 | 30

Ten-second questions

6

7 | 48

8 | 21 31 41

9 | m | $\frac{3}{4}$ km

10 | 6.5

11 | 35p

12 | 12 19 18 11

13 | 51

14 | 6.7

15 | 92 cm

Fifteen-second questions

16 | 13

17

o

18

4 cm

2.5 cm

19 | £20

20 | 10.55 a.m.

Test 7 Answers

Practice question

	4

Five-second questions

1	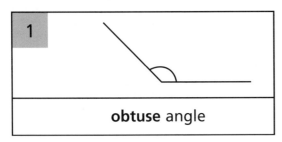
	obtuse angle

2	**170**

3	**23**	11,14,17,20

4	**6**	18

5	**15**	30

Ten-second questions

6	$\frac{7}{8}$	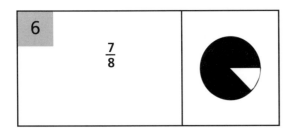

7	**36**	48

8	**93**	21 31 41

9	**750** m	$\frac{3}{4}$ km

10	**0.65**	6.5

11	**£1.05p**	35p

12	**30**	12 19 18 11

13	**3**	51

14	**13.4**	6.7

15	**9**	92 cm

Fifteen-second questions

16	**169**	13

17	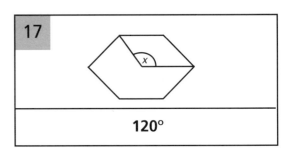
	120°

18	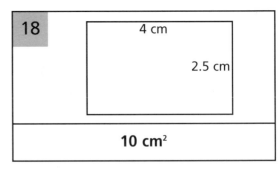
	10 cm²

19	**£5.14**	£20

20	**2 hours 20 minutes**	10.55 a.m.

Test 8

Before playing the test on the CD give each child a copy of the test and read out the following script:

Listen to the instructions carefully. I will answer any questions that you have after I have finished reading the instructions to you. Once the test starts you will not be able to ask any questions.

The first question is a practice question. In the test there will then be twenty questions.

Every question has an answer box. Make sure that you only write the answer to the correct question in the box. Try to work out each answer in your head. You can make notes outside the answer box if this helps you but do not try to write out calculations because you will not have enough time. For some questions you will find important information already provided for you.

Each question will be read out twice. Listen carefully, then work out your answer. If you cannot do the question, just put a cross. If you make a mistake, do not rub out the wrong answer; cross it out and write the correct answer.

Some questions are easy and some are more difficult. Do not worry if you find a question hard; just do your best. I hope that you enjoy the test.

At this point, answer any questions that the children ask.

Now listen carefully to the practice question. You will hear the question twice, then you will have five seconds to work out and write down the answer.

What is double ten?

What is double ten?

Allow the children five seconds to write the answer, then say:

Put your pen down.

Check that the children have written the answer to the practice question in the practice question answer box. Remind them that they cannot ask any more questions once the test is started. When you are ready, press start on your CD player. When the test is finished ask the children to stop writing, then collect the test sheets. For ease of marking we have created a copy of the test paper with the answers entered in the appropriate boxes.

Questions for Test 8

For each of the first five questions you have five seconds to work out and write down the answer.

1 How many days in a leap year?

2 Find the total of seventeen plus twenty-three.

3 What is the value of six times seven?

4 Share sixty between four.

5 How much is thirty-eight minus twenty-seven?

For each of the next questions you have ten seconds to work out and write down the answer.

6 How many days are there in June?

7 What is twelve squared?

8 Look at your test sheet.
Draw a ring around the prime number.

9 Find the value of five thousand nine hundred and thirty-seven add sixty.

10 What number is five hundred less than eight hundred and forty-seven?

11 Write eight hundred and forty-seven grams in kilograms.

12 Look at your test sheet.
What volume of water is shown in the measuring cylinder?

13 What is twenty-five per cent of nine pounds?

14 What time is two hours and ten minutes after nine fifty-five a.m.?

15 What is one point four multiplied by three?

For each of the next questions you have fifteen seconds to work out and write down the answer.

16 A temperature of seven degrees Celsius is recorded.
The temperature drops by twenty degrees Celsius.
What is the new temperature?

17 Look at your test sheet.
Write the size of the angle marked x.

18 Look at your test sheet.
Put a ring around the number that is not a multiple of four.

19 What is twenty-five per cent of five hundred pounds?

20 How much is double nineteen point seven?

Put your pen down. The test is over.

Andrew Brodie: Mental Maths Tests 10–11 © A & C Black

Test 8

First name .... Last name ....

School ....

.... **Total marks**

Practice question

Five-second questions

1		days

2		17	23

3		7

4		60

5		38

Ten-second questions

6		days

7		12

8	33	35	37	39

9		5937

10		847

11		kgs	847

12		ml

500 ml
400
300
200
100

13	£	£9

14		9.55 a.m.

15		1.4

Fifteen-second questions

16		°C	7°C

17	

x 64°

°

18	140	150	160	180

19	£	£500

20		19.7

Test 8 Answers

Practice question

	20

Five-second questions

1	**366** days	

2	**40**	17 23

3	**42**	7

4	**15**	60

5	**11**	38

Ten-second questions

6	**30** days

7	**144**	12

8	33 35 (37) 39

9	**5997**	5937

10	**347**	847

11	**0.847** kgs	847

12	**420** ml	

13	**£2.25p**	£9

14	**12.05 p.m.**	9.55 a.m.

15	**4.2**	1.4

Fifteen-second questions

16	**-13** °C	7 °C

17	
	116 °

18	140 (150) 160 180

19	**£125.00**	£500

20	**39.40**	19.7

Test 9

Before playing the test on the CD give each child a copy of the test and read out the following script:

Listen to the instructions carefully. I will answer any questions that you have after I have finished reading the instructions to you. Once the test starts you will not be able to ask any questions.

The first question is a practice question. In the test there will then be twenty questions.

Every question has an answer box. Make sure that you only write the answer to the correct question in the box. Try to work out each answer in your head. You can make notes outside the answer box if this helps you but do not try to write out calculations because you will not have enough time. For some questions you will find important information already provided for you.

Each question will be read out twice. Listen carefully, then work out your answer. If you cannot do the question, just put a cross. If you make a mistake, do not rub out the wrong answer; cross it out and write the correct answer.

Some questions are easy and some are more difficult. Do not worry if you find a question hard; just do your best. I hope that you enjoy the test.

At this point, answer any questions that the children ask.

Now listen carefully to the practice question. You will hear the question twice, then you will have five seconds to work out and write down the answer.

Subtract nine from twelve.

Subtract nine from twelve.

Allow the children five seconds to write the answer, then say:

Put your pen down.

Check that the children have written the answer to the practice question in the practice question answer box. Remind them that they cannot ask any more questions once the test is started. When you are ready, press start on your CD player. When the test is finished ask the children to stop writing, then collect the test sheets. For ease of marking we have created a copy of the test paper with the answers entered in the appropriate boxes.

Questions for Test 9

For each of the first five questions you have five seconds to work out and write down the answer.

1   Take thirteen away from thirty.

2   Write the number which is fifteen less than one thousand.

3   What is eight multiplied by five?

4   How many eights make sixty-four?

5   What is the sum of three, four and five?

For each of the next questions you have ten seconds to work out and write down the answer.

6   Divide twenty-five into four hundred and fifty.

7   What is five percent of two hundred?

8   A train travels at eighty miles per hour for two and a half hours.
How far does it travel?

9   What is the value of eleven squared?

10   What is the total of three, two, four, one and five?

11   How much is double seven point four?

12   I spend seven pounds eighty-five pence.
How much change do I get from ten pounds?

13   How many seconds are there in five minutes?

14   Divide eight point two by ten.

15   What number is three quarters of twenty-four?

For each of the next questions you have fifteen seconds to work out and write down the answer.

16   Look at your test sheet.
How much water must be added to make a volume of half a litre?

17   What is the mean of six, fourteen and nineteen?

18   Look at your test sheet.
What is the perimeter of the rectangle?

19   The temperature rises by eight degrees from minus three degrees Celsius.
What is the new temperature?

20   Look at the isosceles triangle on your test sheet.
Write down the size of the angle marked *x*.

Put your pen down. The test is over.

     Andrew Brodie: Mental Maths Tests 10–11 © A & C Black

Test 9

First name .... Last name ....

School ....

.... **Total marks**

Practice question

Five-second questions

1		30

2		1000

3		8

4		64

5		3 4 5

Ten-second questions

6		450

7		200

8	miles	80mph $2\frac{1}{2}$ hours

9		11

10		3 2 4 1 5

11		7.4

12	£	£7.85

13	seconds	5 minutes

14		8.2

15		24

Fifteen-second questions

16	ml

17		6 14 19

18	4.2 cm 2.3 cm
	cm

19	°C	8°C

20	

| | ° |

Test 9 Answers

Practice question

	3

Five-second questions

1	**17**	30
2	**985**	1000
3	**40**	8
4	**8**	64
5	**12**	3 4 5

Ten-second questions

6	**18**	450
7	**10**	200
8	**200** miles	80 mph $2\frac{1}{2}$ hours
9	**121**	11
10	**15**	3 2 4 1 5
11	**14.8**	7.4
12	**£2.15**	**£7.85**

13	**300** seconds	5 minutes
14	**0.82**	8.2
15	**18**	24

Fifteen-second questions

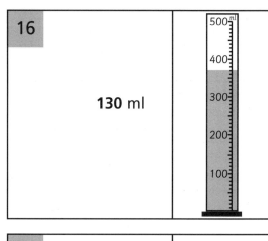

16	**130** ml	

17	**13**	6 14 19

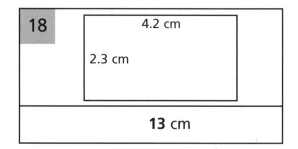

18	**13** cm

19	**5** °C	8 °C

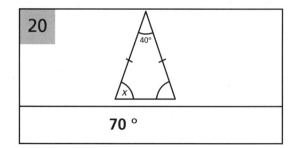

20	**70** °

Test 10

Before playing the test on the CD give each child a copy of the test and read out the following script:

Listen to the instructions carefully. I will answer any questions that you have after I have finished reading the instructions to you. Once the test starts you will not be able to ask any questions.

The first question is a practice question. In the test there will then be twenty questions.

Every question has an answer box. Make sure that you only write the answer to the correct question in the box. Try to work out each answer in your head. You can make notes outside the answer box if this helps you but do not try to write out calculations because you will not have enough time. For some questions you will find important information already provided for you.

Each question will be read out twice. Listen carefully, then work out your answer. If you cannot do the question, just put a cross. If you make a mistake, do not rub out the wrong answer; cross it out and write the correct answer.

Some questions are easy and some are more difficult. Do not worry if you find a question hard; just do your best. I hope that you enjoy the test.

At this point, answer any questions that the children ask.

Now listen carefully to the practice question. You will hear the question twice, then you will have five seconds to work out and write down the answer.

Divide twelve by three.

Divide twelve by three.

Allow the children five seconds to write the answer, then say:

Put your pen down.

Check that the children have written the answer to the practice question in the practice question answer box. Remind them that they cannot ask any more questions once the test is started. When you are ready, press start on your CD player. When the test is finished ask the children to stop writing, then collect the test sheets. For ease of marking we have created a copy of the test paper with the answers entered in the appropriate boxes.

Questions for Test 10

For each of the first five questions you have five seconds to work out and write down the answer.

1   What is the product of six and five?

2   How much is forty-nine divided by seven?

3   What is double thirteen?

4   Add five, seven and nine.

5   Write the number twenty-six thousand, four hundred and eight.

For each of the next questions you have ten seconds to work out and write down the answer.

6   What is the remainder when forty-seven is divided by five?

7   How much is six hundred and thirty-seven take away two hundred and six?

8   What is the value of half of seventy-two?

9   Find the sum of five hundred, six hundred and seven hundred.

10   Look at your test sheet.
          Write the size of the angle marked x.

11   Write the next number in this sequence: twenty-two, nineteen, sixteen.

12   Five times a number is three hundred.
          What is the number?

13   How many metres are there in two and a half kilometres?

14   Look at your test sheet.
          Draw a ring around the fraction that is worth the same as one half.

15   Look at your test sheet.
          What is the area of the square?

For each of the next questions you have fifteen seconds to work out and write down the answer.

16   What is half of seven hundred and forty-two pounds?

17   Look at the regular pentagon on your test sheet.
          What size is the angle marked y?

18   What number is halfway between four hundred and eight hundred?

19   What is two thousand take away one hundred and fifty?

20   How much time between nine thirty a.m. and two fifteen p.m.?

Put your pen down. The test is over.

Andrew Brodie: Mental Maths Tests 10–11 © A & C Black

Test 10

First name .... Last name ....

School ....

....

Total marks

Practice question

Five-second questions

| 1 | | 6   5 |

| 2 | | 49 |

| 3 | | 13 |

| 4 | | 5   7   9 |

| 5 | |

Ten-second questions

| 6 | | 47 |

| 7 | | 637 |

| 8 | | 72 |

| 9 | | 500   600   700 |

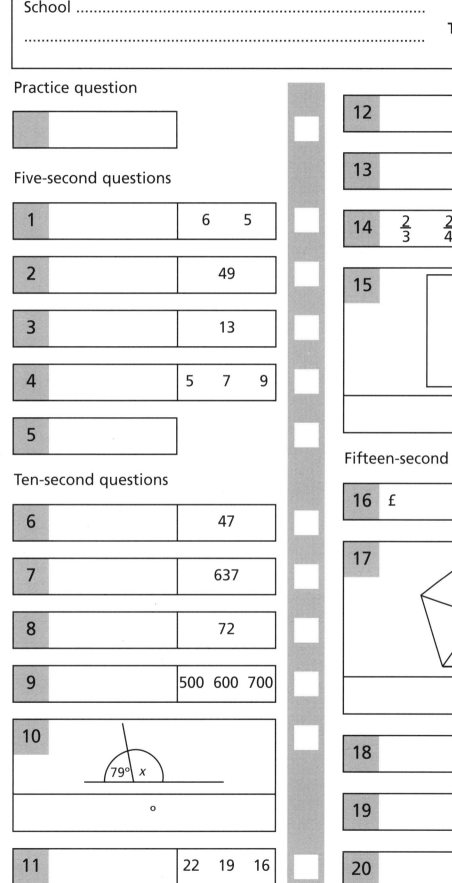

| 10 | 79° x |
| | ° |

| 11 | | 22   19   16 |

| 12 | | 300 |

| 13 | | m | $2\frac{1}{2}$ km |

| 14 | $\frac{2}{3}$ | $\frac{2}{4}$ | $\frac{2}{5}$ | $\frac{2}{6}$ | $\frac{2}{1}$ |

| 15 | 6 cm |

Fifteen-second questions

| 16 | £ | £742 |

| 17 | y | ° |

| 18 | | 400   800 |

| 19 | | 2000 |

| 20 | | 9.30 a.m. |

Test 10 Answers

Practice question

	4

Five-second questions

1	30	6	5

2	7	49

3	26	13

4	21	5	7	9

5	26408

Ten-second questions

6	2	47

7	431	637

8	36	72

9	1800	500 600 700

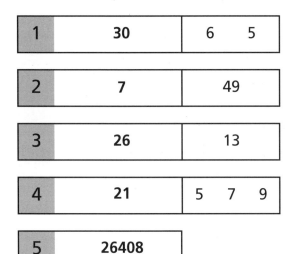

10	
	101°

11	13	22 19 16

12	60	300

13	2500 m	$2\frac{1}{2}$ km

14	$\frac{2}{3}$	$\frac{2}{4}$	$\frac{2}{5}$	$\frac{2}{6}$	$\frac{2}{1}$

15	
	6 cm
36 cm²	

Fifteen-second questions

16	£371	£742

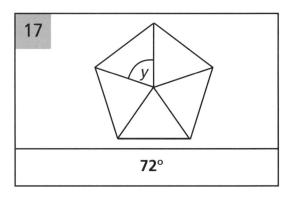

17	
	72°

18	600	400 800

19	1850	2000

20	4 hours 45 min	9.30 a.m.

Pupil Record Sheet

You may wish to record your pupils' scores as they complete each test .

We supply a record sheet on which you can enter the pupils' names down the left hand column and the dates of the tests along the top.

It is worth observing where the pupils are making errors. Errors may occur on particular types of question, perhaps where certain vocabulary is used. Is there a pattern to their problems?

You may also find that some pupils find the time restrictions challenging. Do they find the five-second questions more difficult, for example, simply due to the speed with which they have to answer?

Where patterns do emerge you will be able to target your teaching to address the pupils' needs. You should then find improvements as the pupils work through the set of tests.

Pupil Record Sheet

Class ....

Test number:	1	2	3	4	5	6	7	8	9	10
Date:										

Multiplication Grids

Name..

How quickly can you complete these multiplication grids?

X	1	2	3	4	5	6	7	8	9	10
1										
2										
3										
4										
5										
6										
7										
8										
9										
10										

X	1	2	3	4	5	6	7	8	9	10
25										
50										
75										

Mixed up Multiplication Grids

Name...

How quickly can you complete these multiplication grids?

X	7	4	8	3	5	10	1	9	2	6
3										
9										
1										
4										
7										
10										
2										
5										
6										
8										

X	7	3	8	10	6	4	2	1	9	5
25										
50										
75										

Addition Grids

Name...

How quickly can you complete these addition grids?

+	11	12	13	14	15	16	17	18	19	20
11										
12										
13										
14										
15										
16										
17										
18										
19										
20										

+	75	25	35	85	65	45	15	55	5	95
25										
50										
75										

Mixed multiplication squares

Name...

x	2	7	3	9	4	6	8	5	10
6									
5									
9									
3									
7									
2									
8									
4									
10									

x	50	100	75	200	25
4					
2					
3					
1					
5					

 Andrew Brodie: Mental Maths Tests 10–11 © A & C Black